MATH CONCEPTS

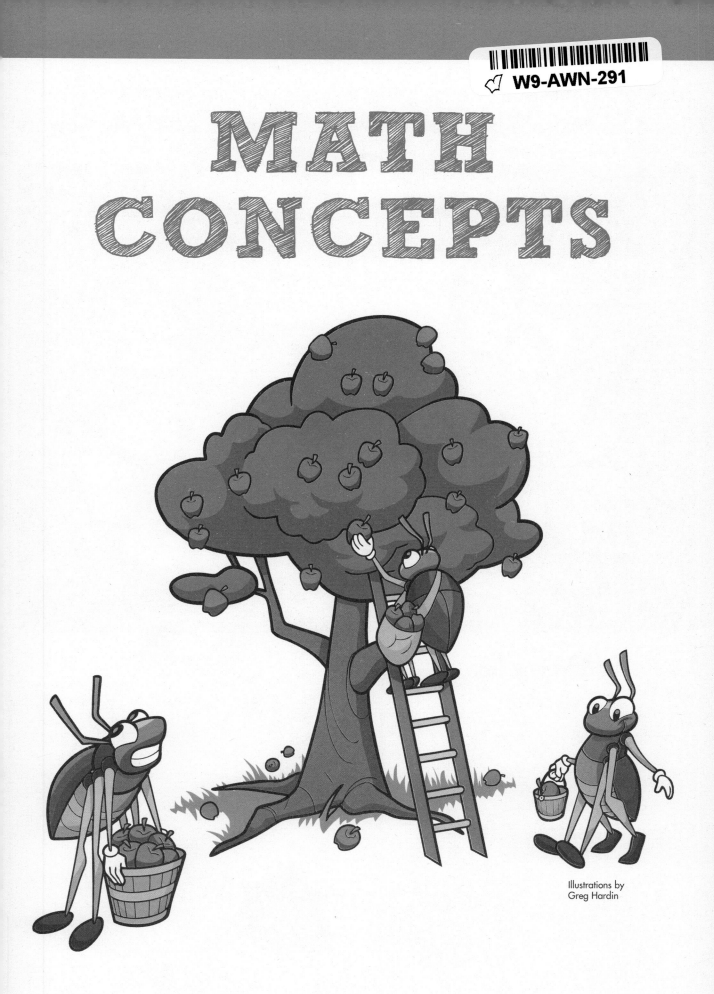

Illustrations by
Greg Hardin

Look at all the busy bees gathering nectar from flowers.
Some flowers are **big**. Some flowers are **small**. Color the **flowers**.

Circle the **biggest bee**.

Circle the **smallest flower**.

Draw **stems** for the flowers.
Some are **tall**. Some are **short**. Circle the **shortest flower**.

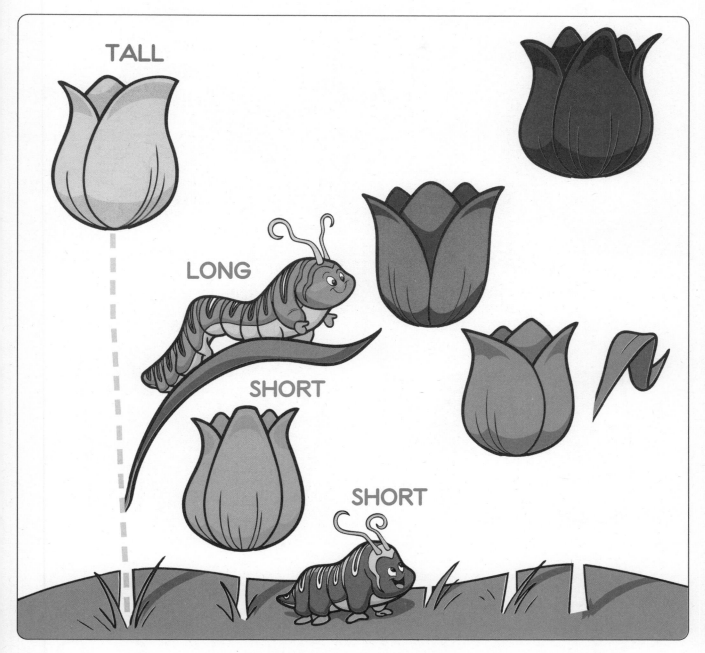

TALL

LONG

SHORT

SHORT

Circle the **longest caterpillar**. Color the **shortest caterpillar**.

Concepts of Volume–More and Less

The busy beetles are making apple juice.

Circle the glass that has **less** juice.

Circle the basket that can hold **more** apples.

for busy thinkers

One apple makes this much juice.

How much juice will two apples make? Color the juice.

Concept of Weight

Some apple baskets are **heavy**! Some apple baskets are **light**.

Circle the apple basket that weighs the **most**.

Circle the plate of fruit that weighs the **least**.

Number Sequencing

The ants are marching one by one!
They are carrying the numbers from 1 to 10. Trace the numbers.

Follow the path from 1 to 10 to help the ant get to the picnic.

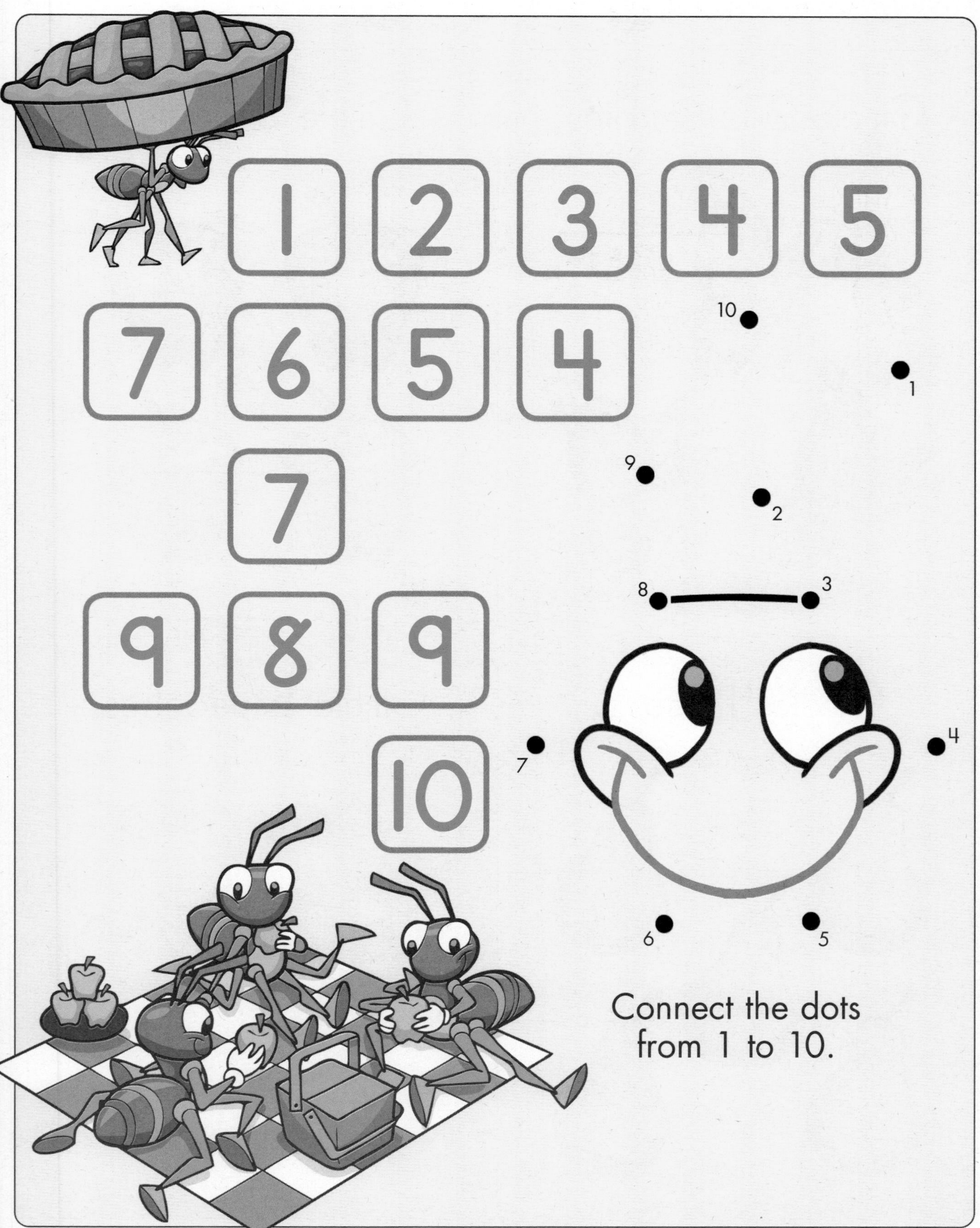

Connect the dots from 1 to 10.

1 2 3 4 5 6 7 8 9 10

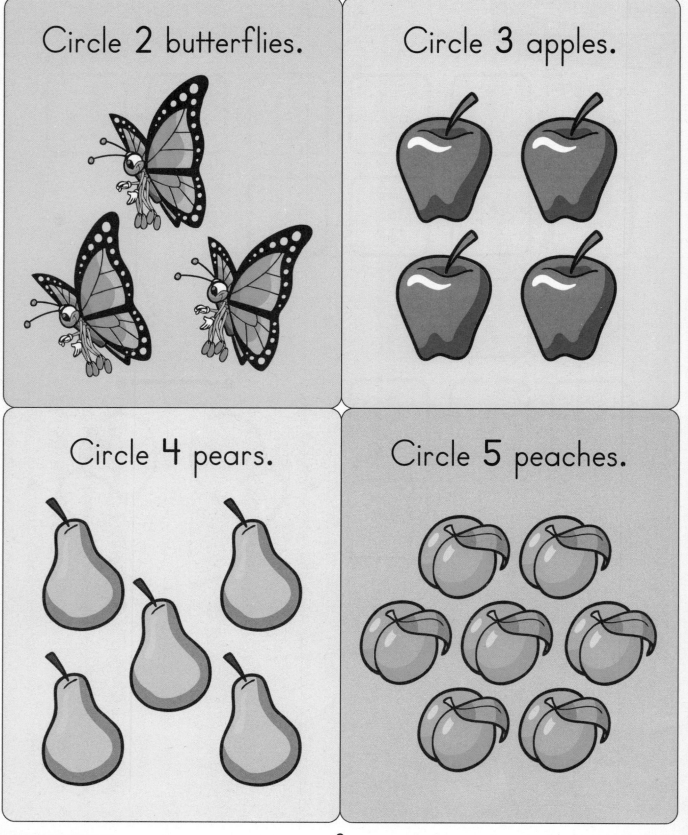

Circle 2 butterflies.

Circle 3 apples.

Circle 4 pears.

Circle 5 peaches.

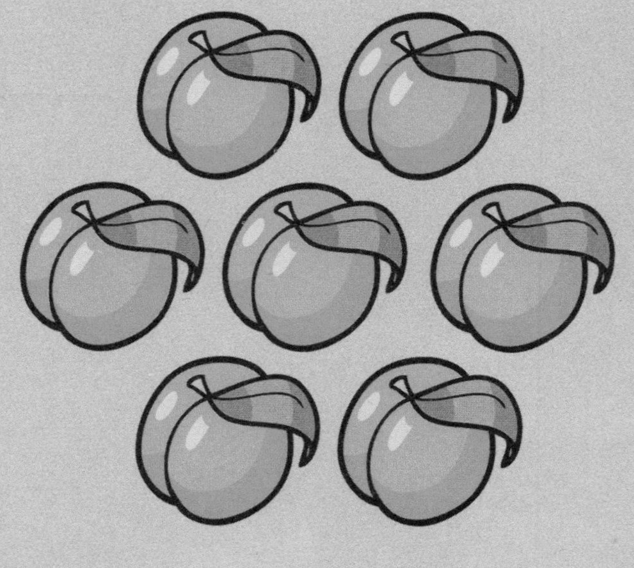

1 2 3 4 5 6 7 8 9 10

Circle 3 bees.

Circle 4 oranges.

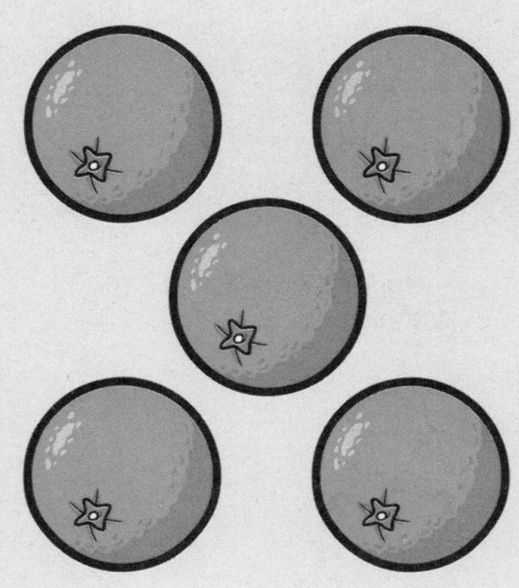

Circle 2 lemons.

Circle 5 strawberries.

Numerical Quantity

Trace and say the number. Count and find a set that has that many. Draw a line from the number to the set.

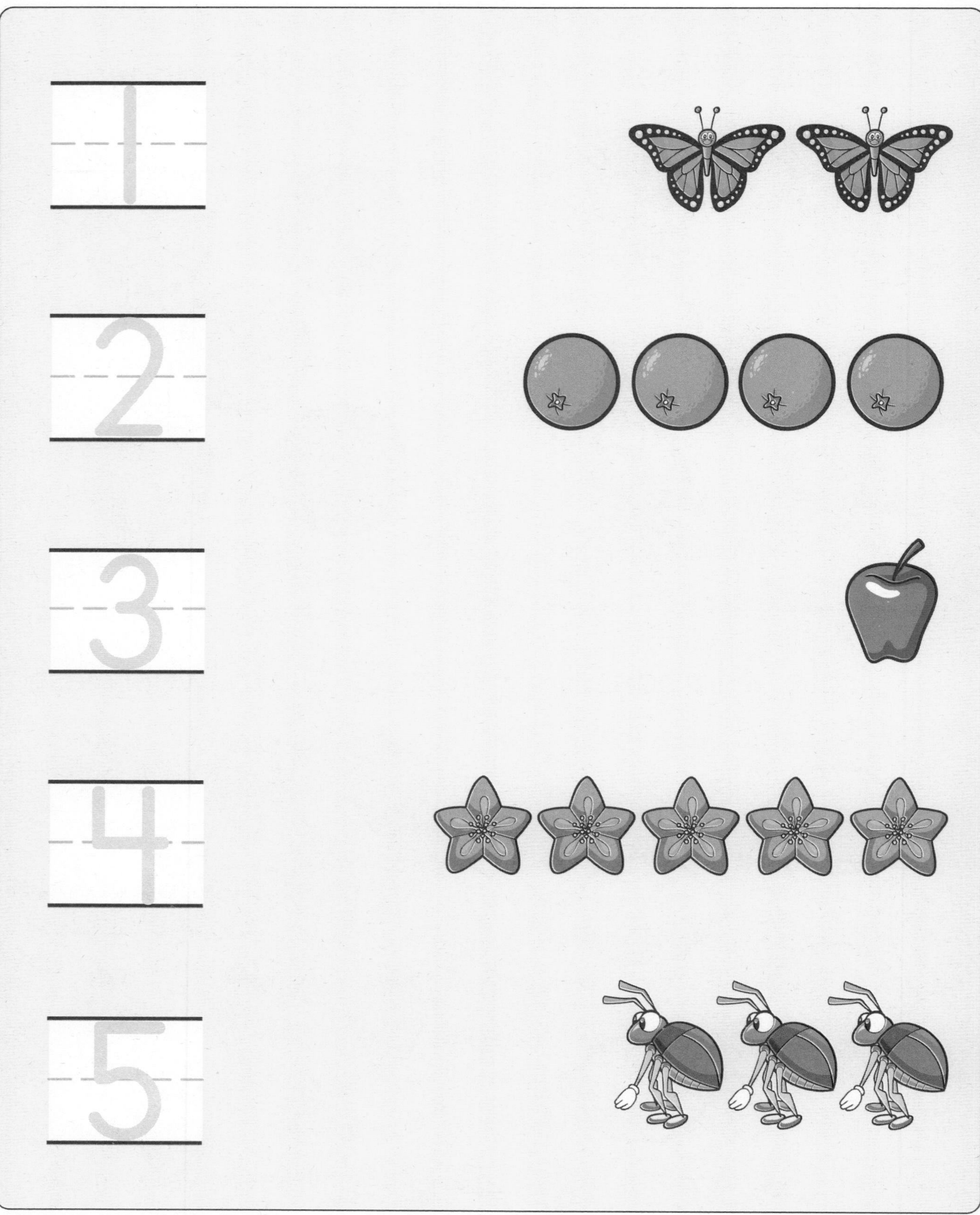

Trace and say the number. Count and find a set that has that many. Draw a line from the number to the set.

3 4 5 6

Count the **oranges** and the **apples**. How many in all?

6 7 8

Circle your answer.

More and Fewer

Welcome to the market! Count the **beetles**. Count the **ants**. Are there **more beetles** or **more ants**?

Circle your answer.

Circle the group that has **more**.

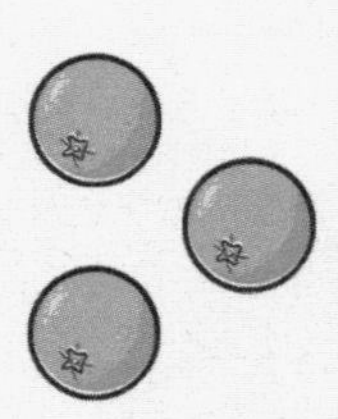

Circle the group that has **fewer**.

Circle the group that has **more**.

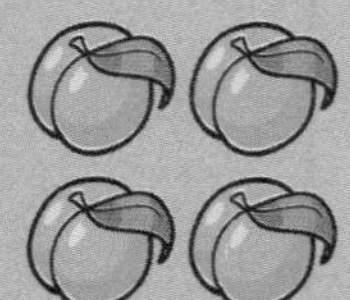

Circle the group that has **fewer**.

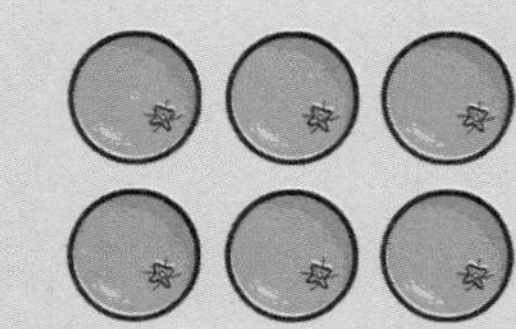

Circle the butterfly with the **most** spots.

Circle the plate with the **most** apples.

Circle the flower with the **fewest** petals.

Circle the watermelon with the **fewest** seeds.

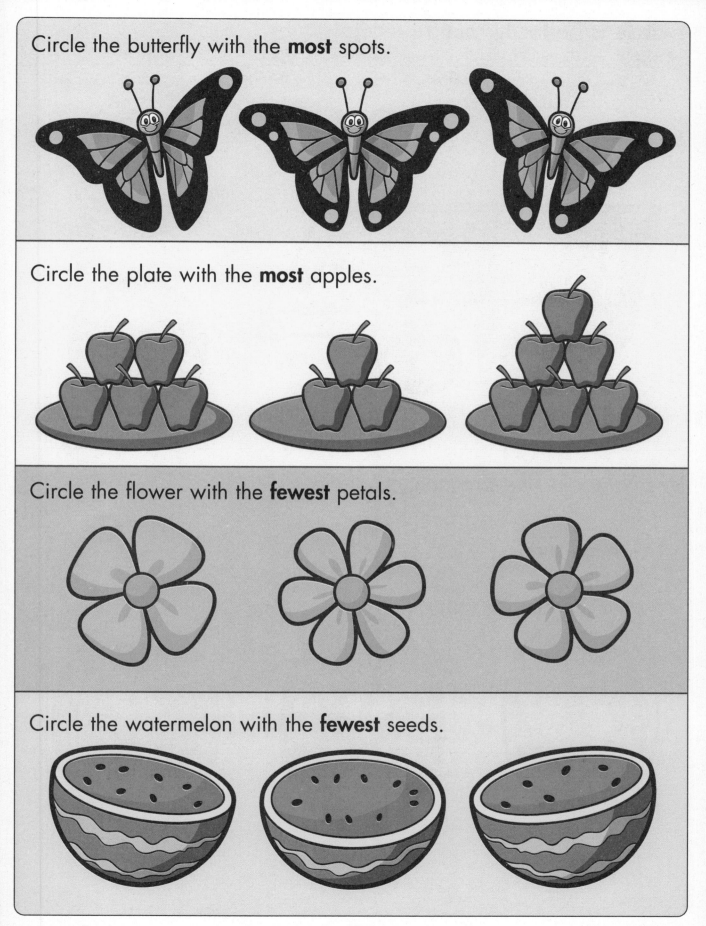

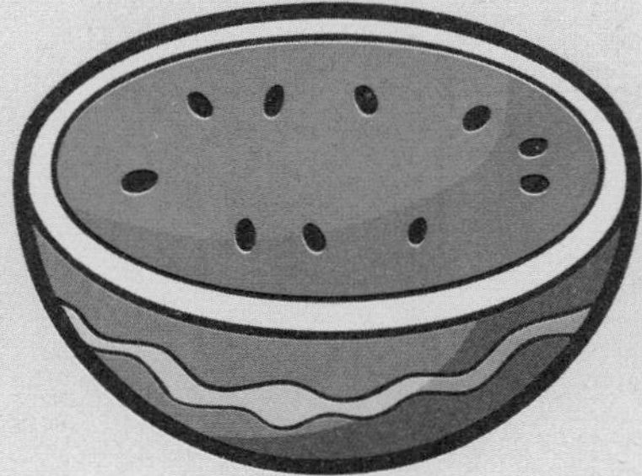

Circle and Oval

A **circle** is perfectly round.

Trace the **circles**.

An **oval** looks like a squashed circle.

Trace the **ovals**.

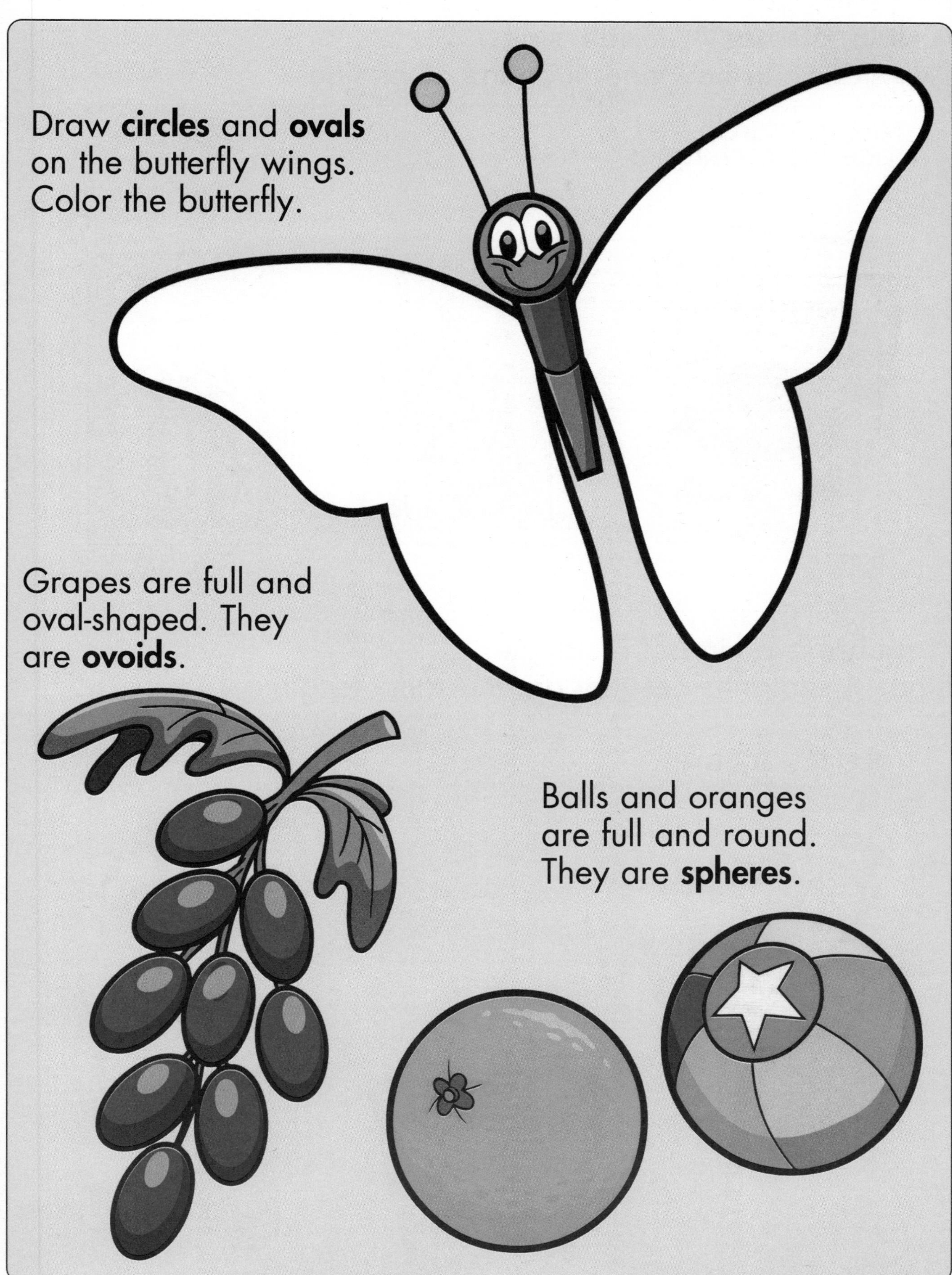

Draw **circles** and **ovals** on the butterfly wings. Color the butterfly.

Grapes are full and oval-shaped. They are **ovoids**.

Balls and oranges are full and round. They are **spheres**.

A **rectangle** has 4 straight sides.
Two sides can be longer than the other sides.

Trace the **rectangles**.

A **square** is a kind of rectangle.
It has 4 straight sides that are the same length.

Trace the **squares**.

Fresh Fruit!

Pears and Peaches!

Some things have sides that are rectangles.
This shape is called a **prism**.

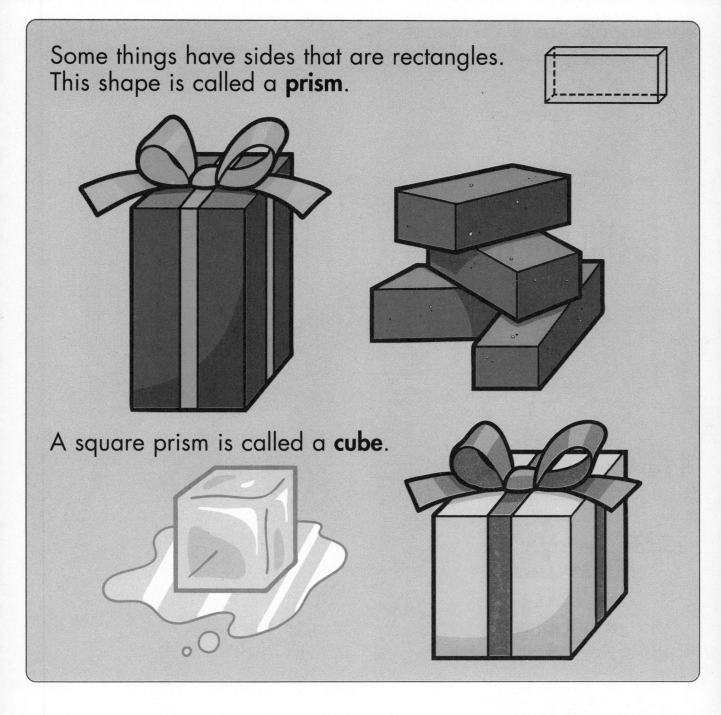

A square prism is called a **cube**.

Draw a circle around each **square**.

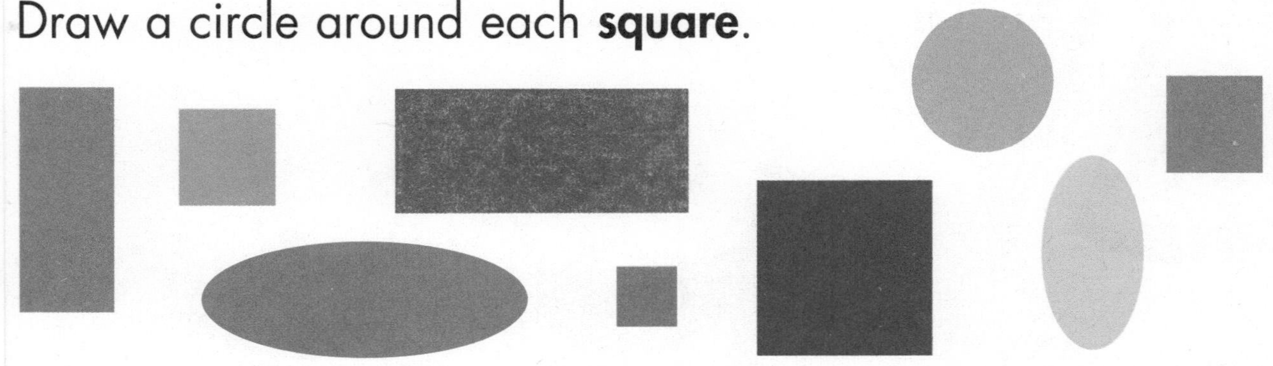

Triangle and Cone

A **triangle** has 3 straight sides.

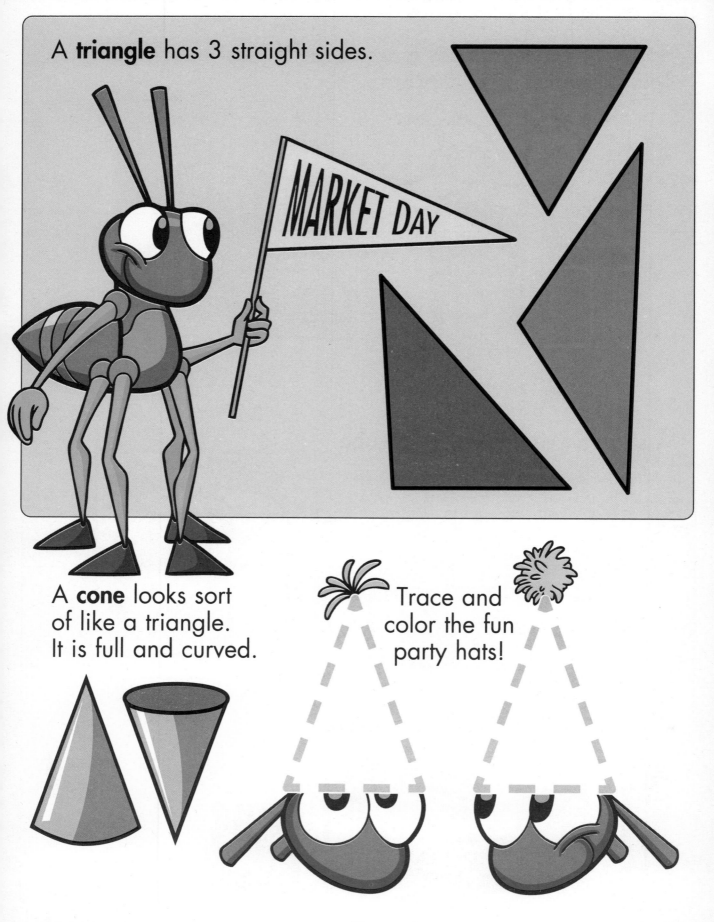

A **cone** looks sort
of like a triangle.
It is full and curved.

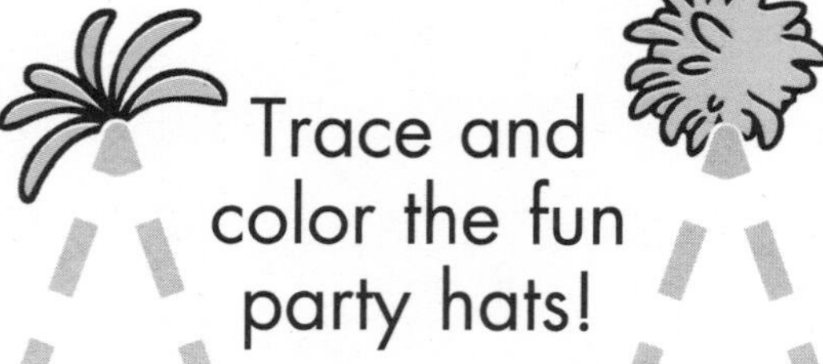

Trace and
color the fun
party hats!

Look at the first **shape**.
Then circle the matching **shape** in its row.

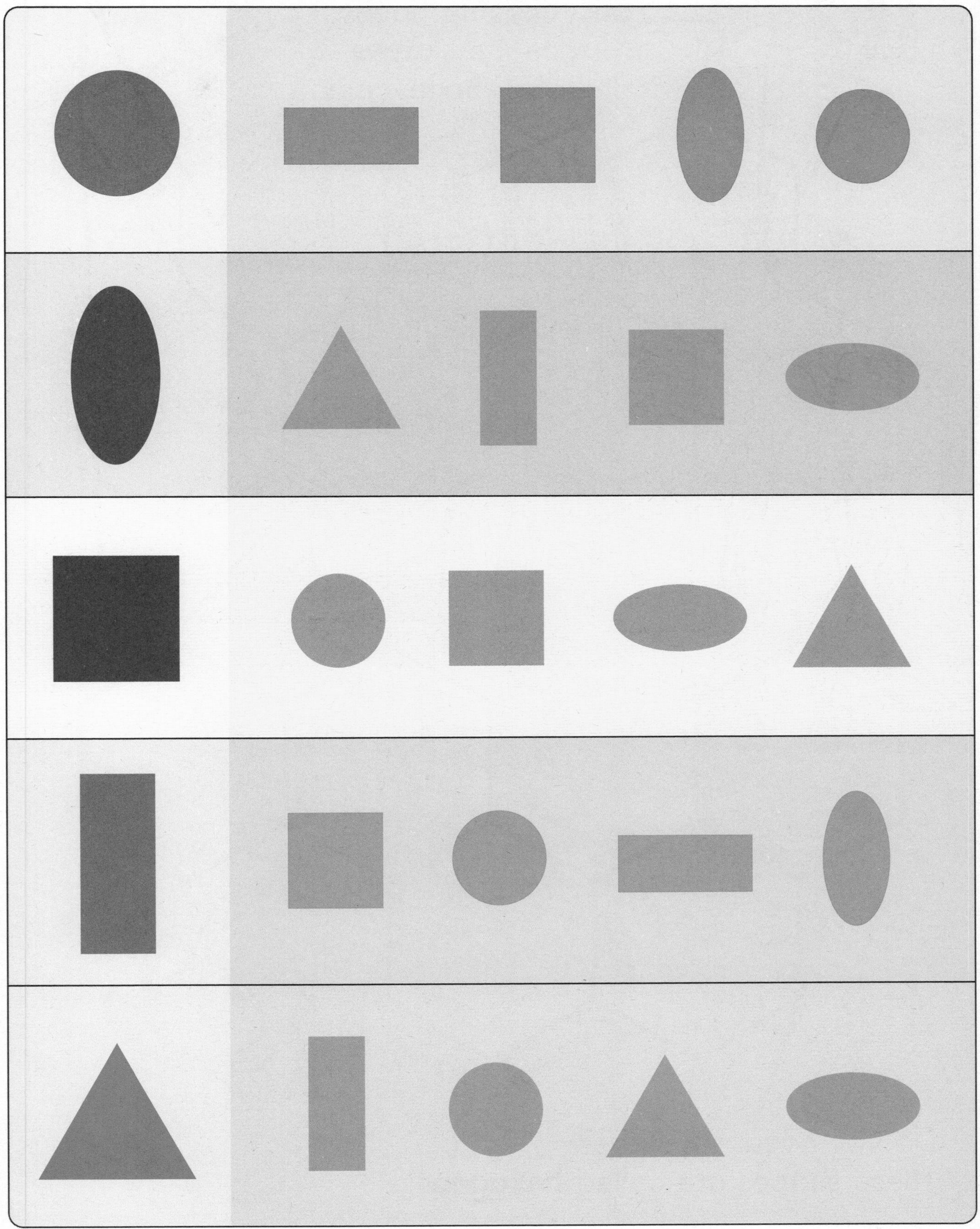

The bees are
busy making honey.
Trace the **shapes**
in their big honeycomb.
Do you count **six** sides?
These shapes are called **hexagons**.

3D Spatial Reasoning

Each of these objects can be built using shapes. Can you tell which shapes can build each object? Draw lines to match the shapes to the objects.

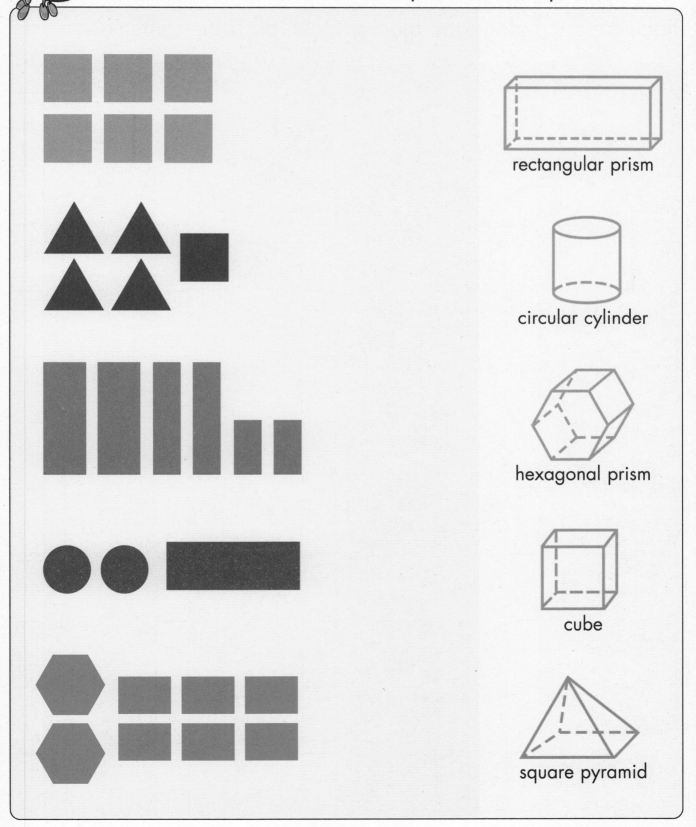

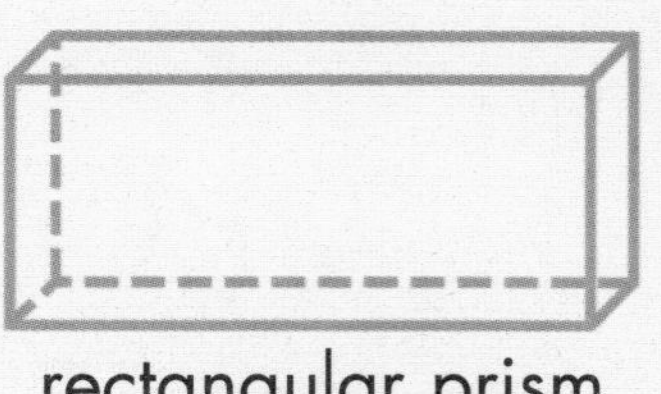
rectangular prism

circular cylinder

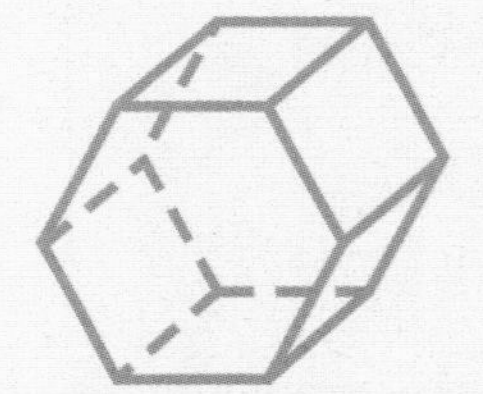
hexagonal prism

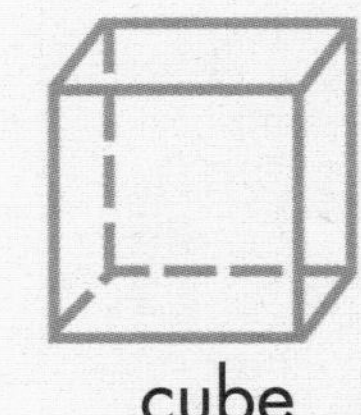
cube

square pyramid

This column of apples is very **tall**!
Color the blocks to show how **tall** the apple column is.
How **tall** is the beetle ladder? Color the blocks.
How **tall** is the flower?
Place a pencil along the blocks. How **tall** is the pencil?

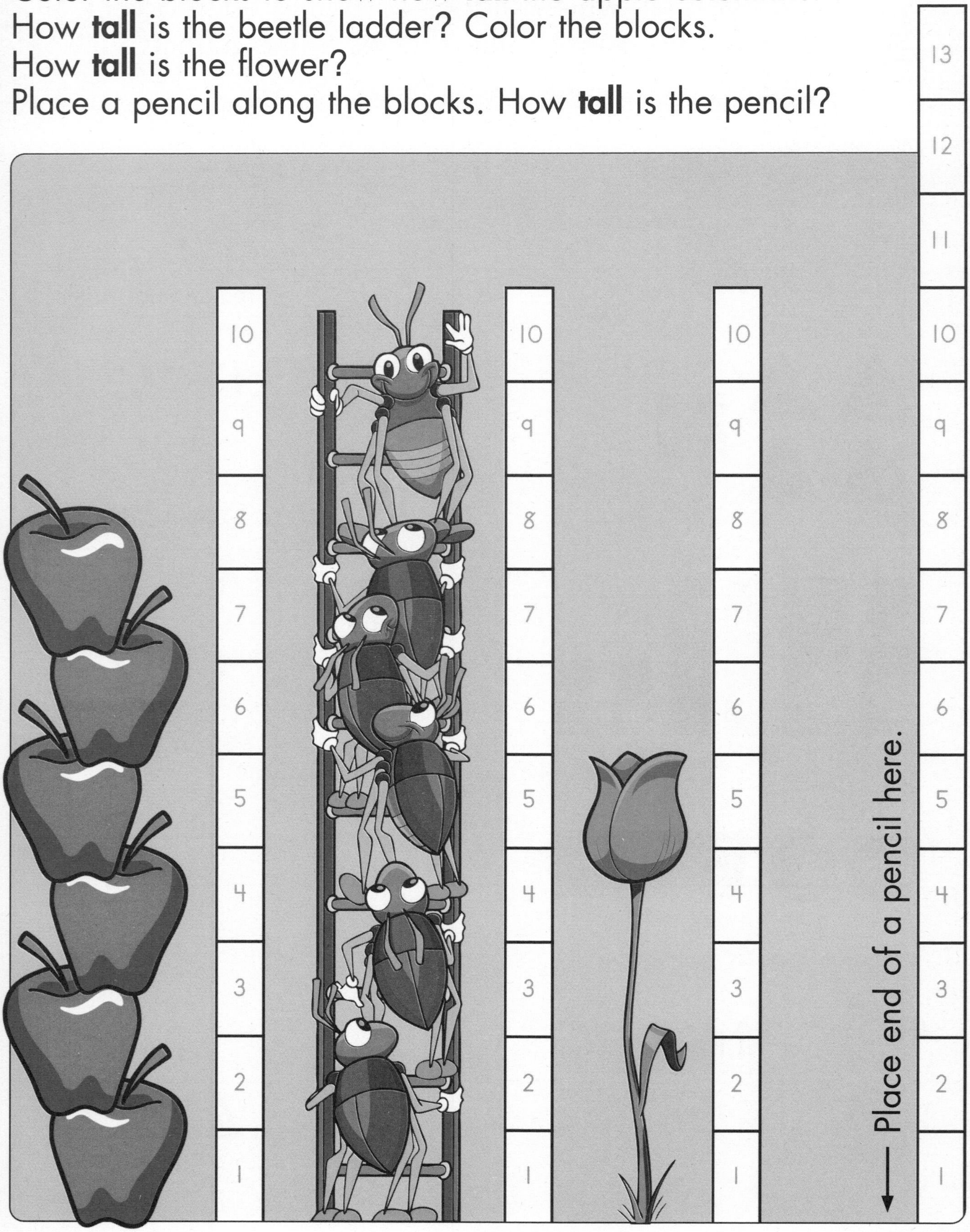

Place end of a pencil here.

This row of apples is very **long**!
Color the blocks to show how **long** the apple row is.

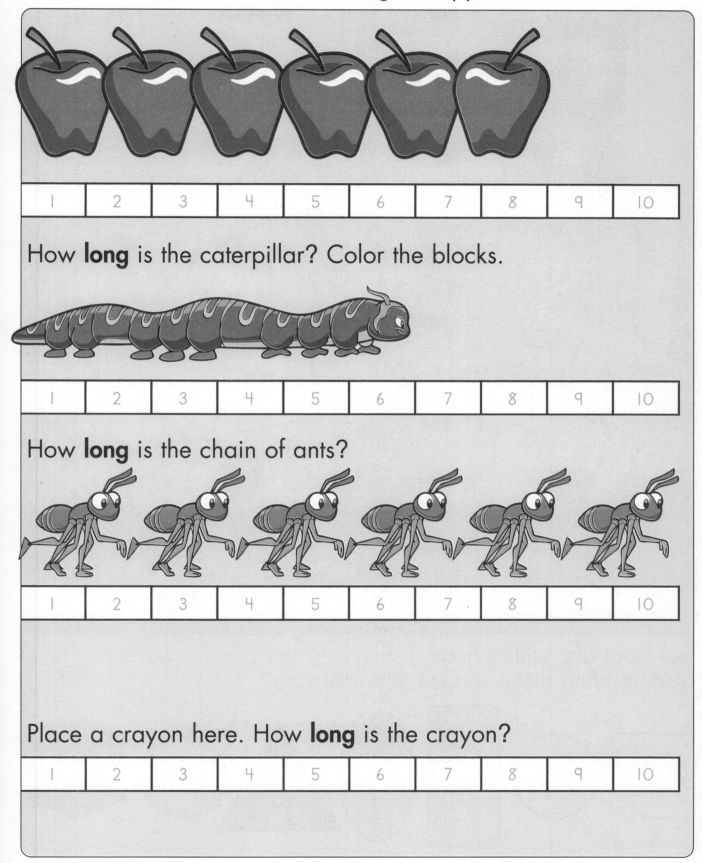

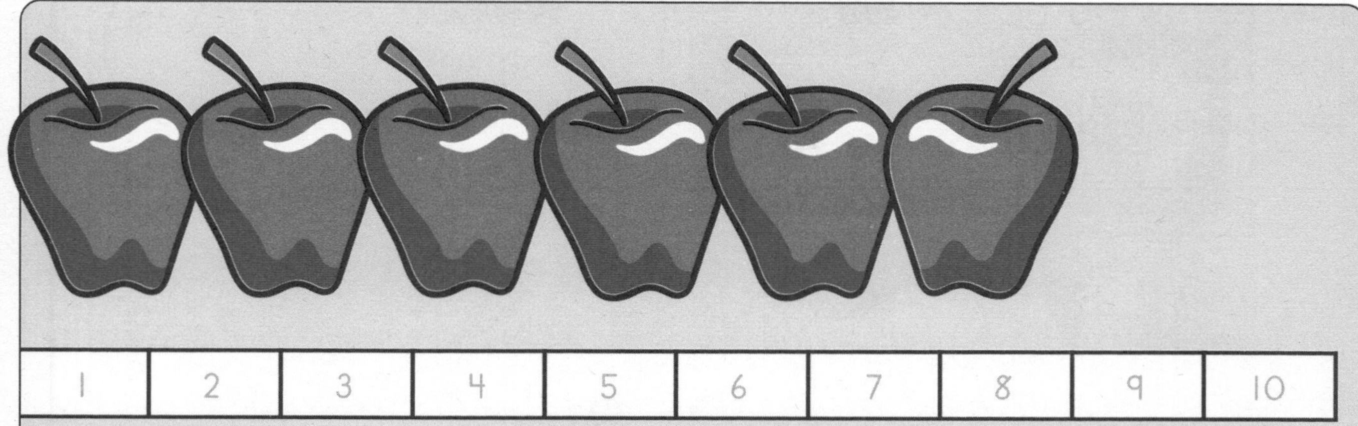

1	2	3	4	5	6	7	8	9	10

How **long** is the caterpillar? Color the blocks.

1	2	3	4	5	6	7	8	9	10

How **long** is the chain of ants?

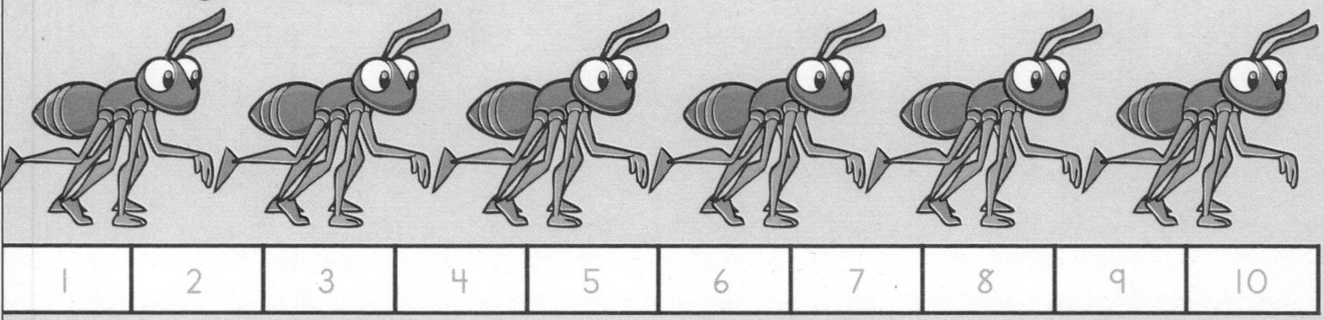

1	2	3	4	5	6	7	8	9	10

Place a crayon here. How **long** is the crayon?

1	2	3	4	5	6	7	8	9	10

The bees are selling honey.
Can you find these **shapes** in the picture?

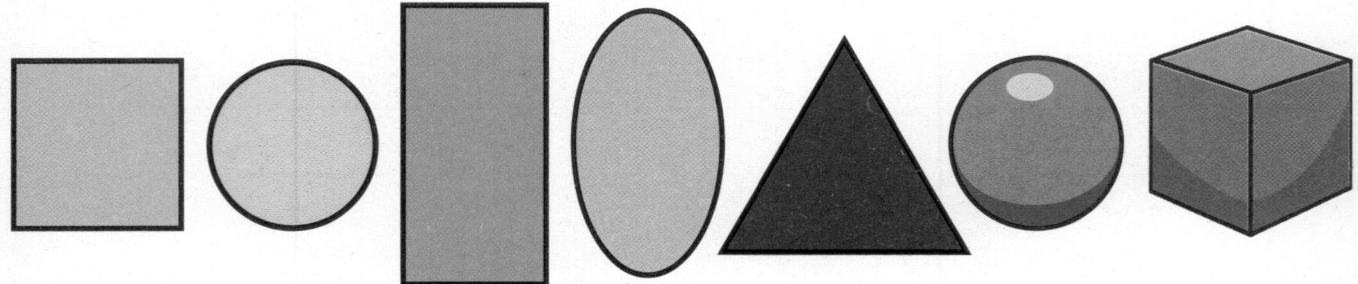

Look at each row of numbers.
Which number is missing in the **sequence**? Circle the answer.

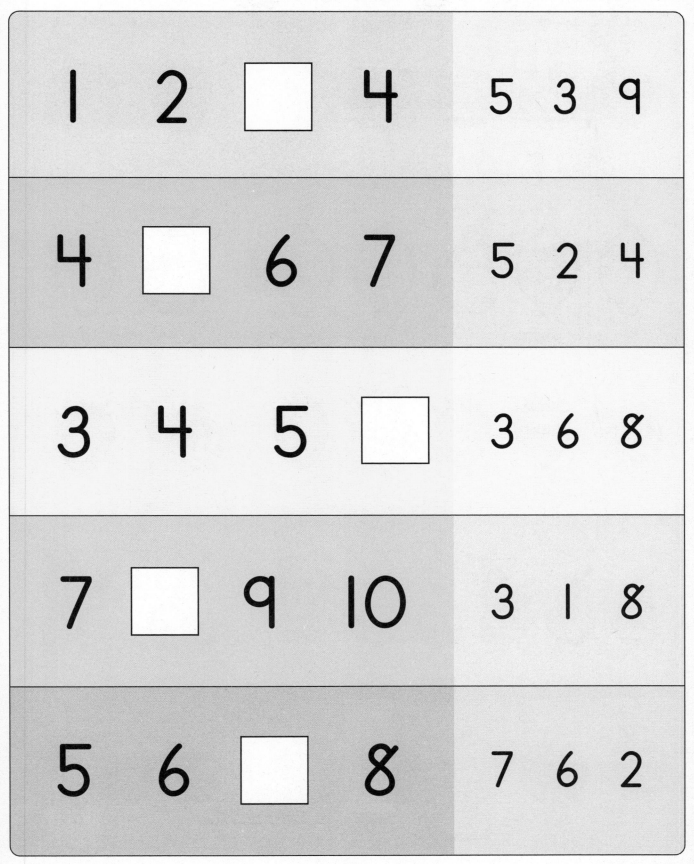

1	2	☐	4	5	3	9
4	☐	6	7	5	2	4
3	4	5	☐	3	6	8
7	☐	9	10	3	1	8
5	6	☐	8	7	6	2

Recognizing Patterns

Look at each row of objects. They each have a pattern.
Circle what comes next in each pattern.

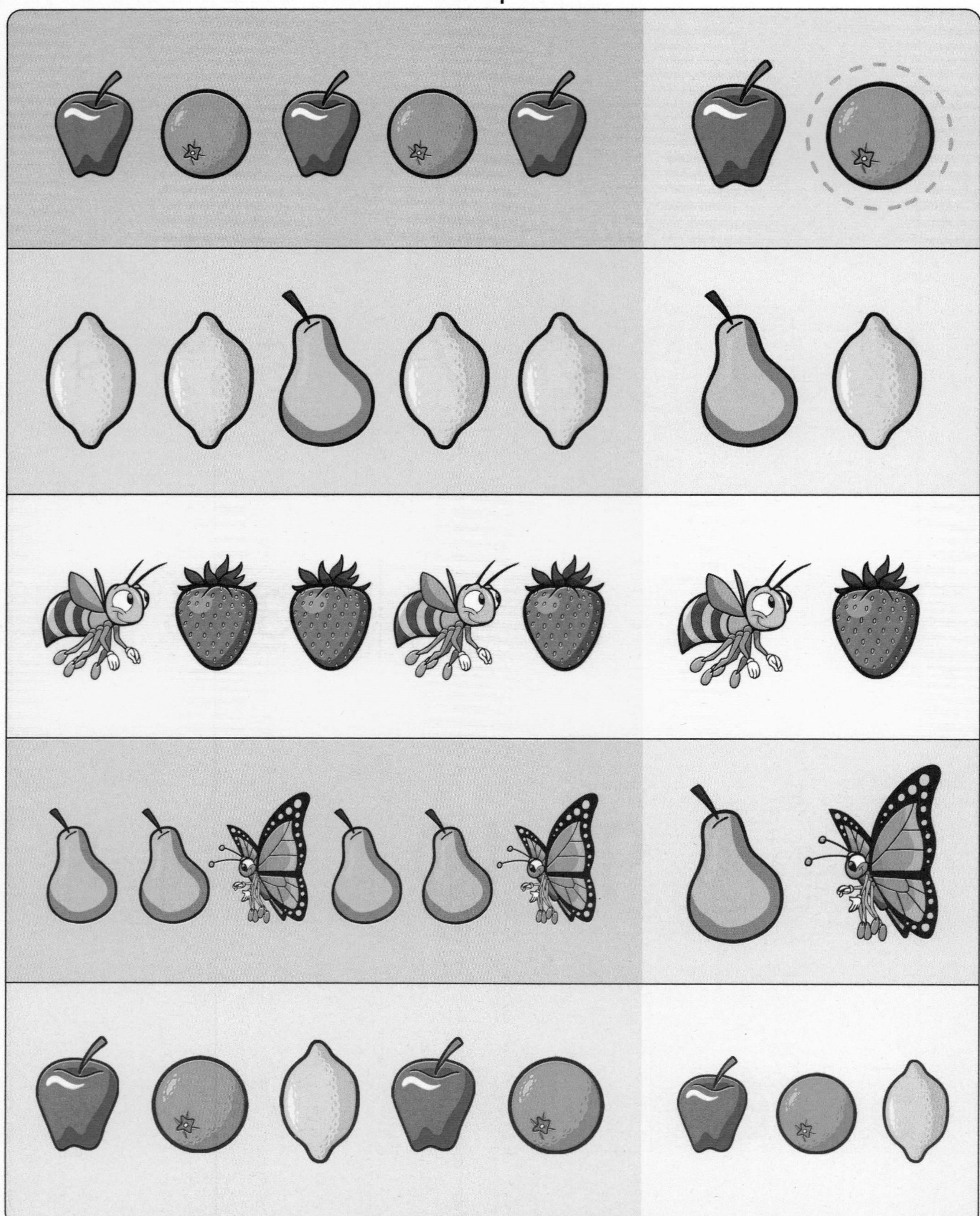

Look at each row of objects.
Circle what comes next in each pattern.

Find and color each **shape**. Use this key for the **shape colors**.

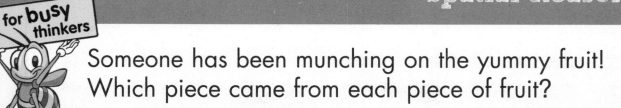

for busy thinkers

Someone has been munching on the yummy fruit!
Which piece came from each piece of fruit?

The bugs are having a big sale!

BIG SALE

2¢ 5¢ 5¢ 10¢ 6¢ 8¢ 3¢

Circle the answer.

What costs the **most**?

What costs the **most**?

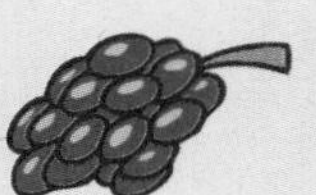

What costs the **least**?

What two things cost the **same**?

Circle how many pennies you need to buy each item.

Draw and Color!

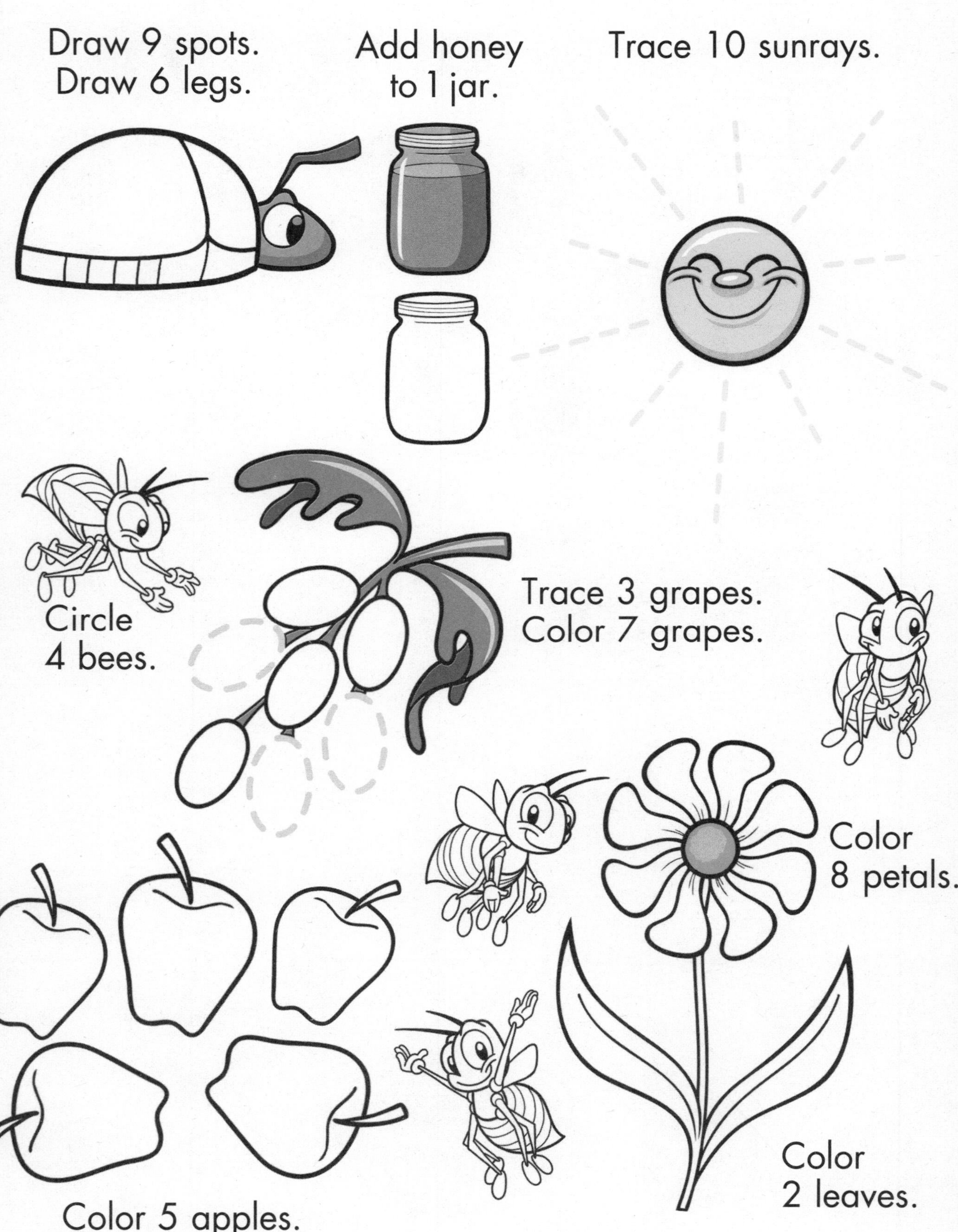

Draw 9 spots.
Draw 6 legs.
Add honey
to 1 jar.
Trace 10 sunrays.
Circle
4 bees.
Trace 3 grapes.
Color 7 grapes.
Color
8 petals.
Color
2 leaves.
Color 5 apples.